THE CHRISTMAS

Activity Book For Kids

AGES 4-6

THIS WONDERFUL BOOK BELONGS TO:

_____

FOLLOW THE NUMBERS IN ORDER TO CREATE THE PICTURE!

START HERE

DECORATE AND BRING YOUR OWN SNOWMAN TO LIFE!

Time to hang the wreath! Find your way through the maze to the center!

TRACE THE DOTTED LINES AND COLOR THE PICTURE!

FOLLOW THE NUMBERS IN ORDER TO CREATE THE PICTURE!

DESIGN the CHRISTMAS COOKIES!

FIND YOUR WAY THROUGH THE SNOWMAN TO HELP BUILD HIM!

START

FINISH

TRACE THE DOTTED LINES AND COLOR THE PICTURE!

FOLLOW THE NUMBERS IN ORDER TO CREATE THE PICTURE!

16

Help the Elf design all the cool Christmas toys!

HELP SANTA FIND HIS WAY THROUGH THE CHIMNEY TO GET INSIDE!

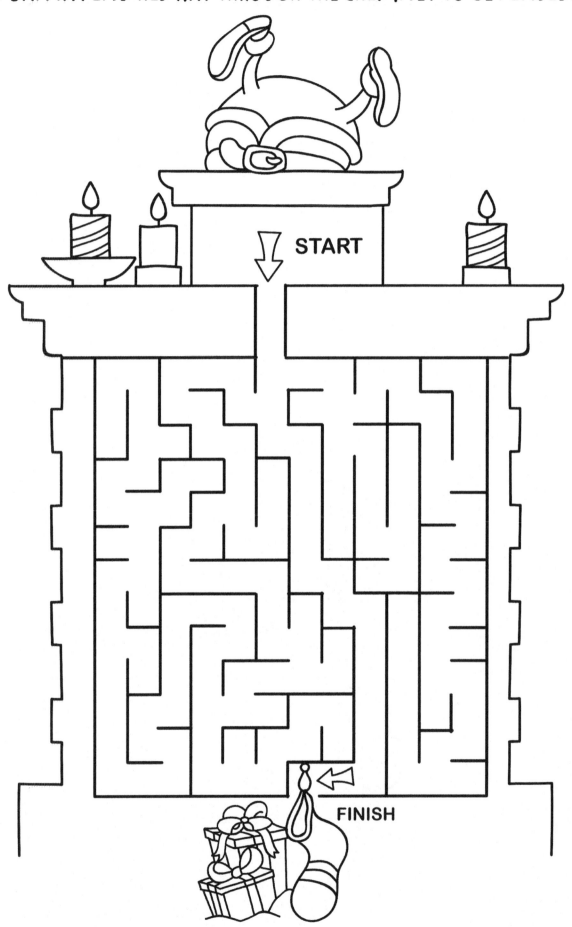

START

FINISH

TRACE THE DOTTED LINES AND COLOR THE PICTURE!

FOLLOW THE NUMBERS IN ORDER TO CREATE THE PICTURE!

START HERE

TIME TO DECORATE THE TREE! DESIGN THE CHRISTMAS ORNAMENTS TO MAKE EACH ONE UNIQUE!

FIND YOUR WAY THROUGH THE CHRISTMAS TREE TO PUT THE TREE TOPPER ON!

FINISH

START

TRACE THE DOTTED LINES AND COLOR THE PICTURE!

FOLLOW THE NUMBERS IN ORDER TO CREATE THE PICTURE!

HELP SANTA BY DRAWING HIS SLEIGH!

Help Santa find his way through his bag of gifts!

FINISH

START

TRACE THE DOTTED LINES AND COLOR THE PICTURE!

FOLLOW THE NUMBERS IN ORDER TO CREATE THE PICTURE!

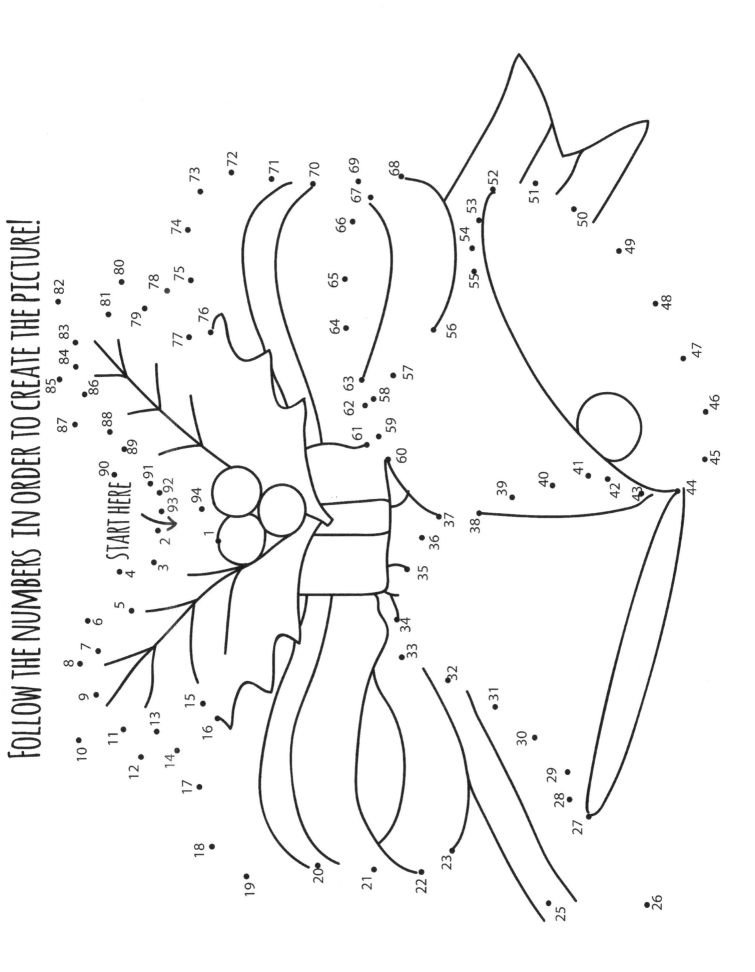

START HERE

DESIGN THE NUTCRACKER AND GIVE HIM A NAME!

Time to decorate the tree! Find your way through the ornament!

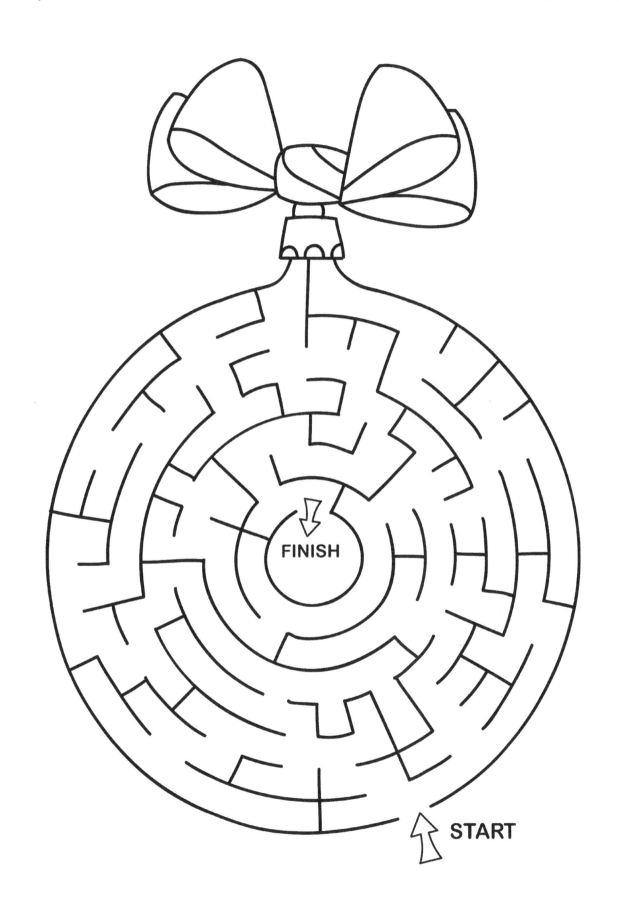

FINISH

START

TRACE THE DOTTED LINES AND COLOR THE PICTURE!

FOLLOW THE NUMBERS IN ORDER TO CREATE THE PICTURE!

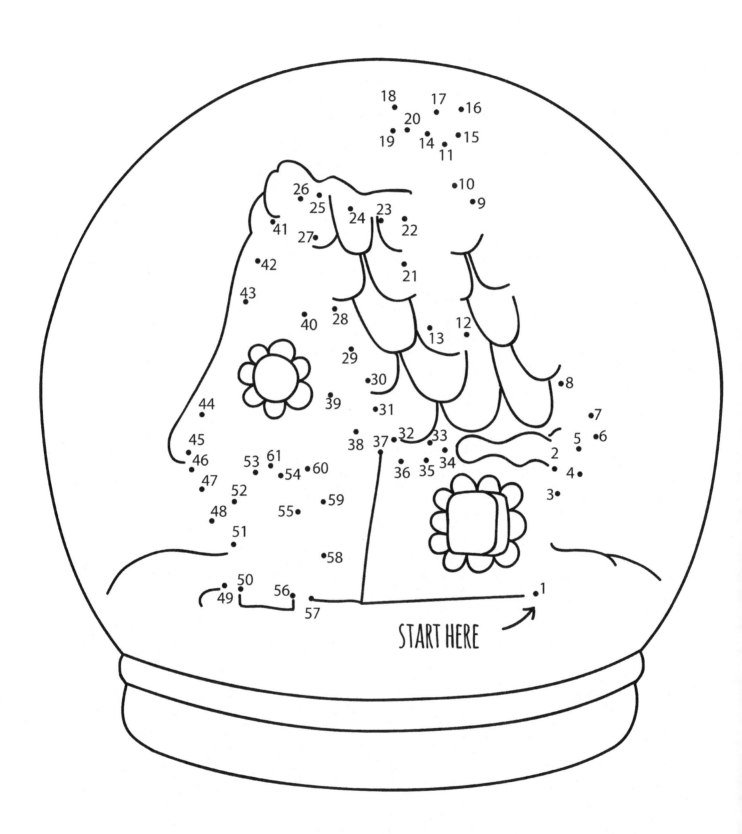

START HERE

FINISH DRAWING AND DECORATE THE GINGERBREAD HOUSE!

FIND YOUR WAY THROUGH SANTA`S HAT!

TRACE THE DOTTED LINES AND COLOR THE PICTURE!

FOLLOW THE NUMBERS IN ORDER TO CREATE THE PICTURE!

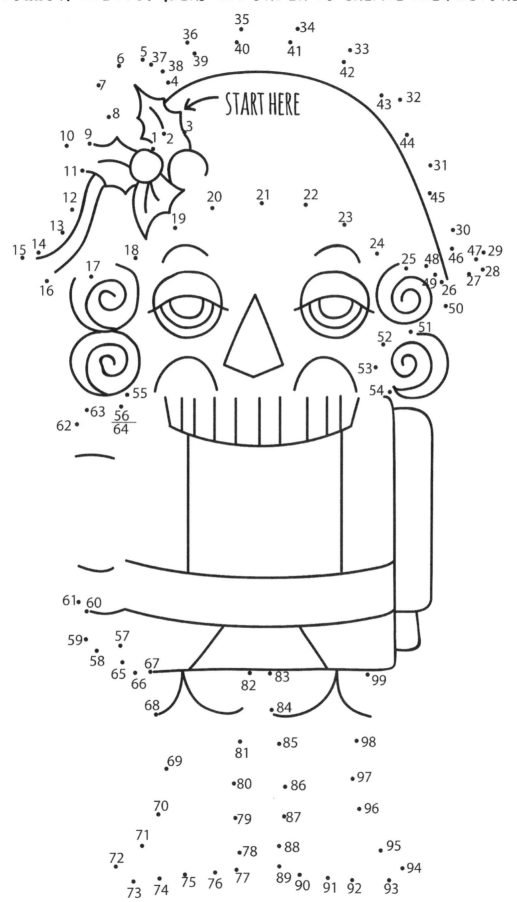

START HERE

CREATE YOUR OWN FUNNY OR UGLY CHRISTMAS SWEATER!

HELP THE LITTLE GIRL FIND HER WAY TO THE TOP OF THE STOCKING TO SEE WHAT'S INSIDE!

FINISH

START

TRACE THE DOTTED LINES AND COLOR THE PICTURE!

FOLLOW THE NUMBERS IN ORDER TO CREATE THE PICTURE!

START HERE →

DESIGN YOUR OWN WINTER CLOTHES!

HELP THE BOY FIND HIS WAY THROUGH THE HOUSE TO GO OUTSIDE AND PLAY!

START

FINISH

TRACE THE DOTTED LINES AND COLOR THE PICTURE!

FOLLOW THE NUMBERS IN ORDER TO CREATE THE PICTURE!

START HERE →

Decorate the Christmas tree!

FIND YOUR WAY THROUGH THE PRESENT TO SEE WHAT'S INSIDE!

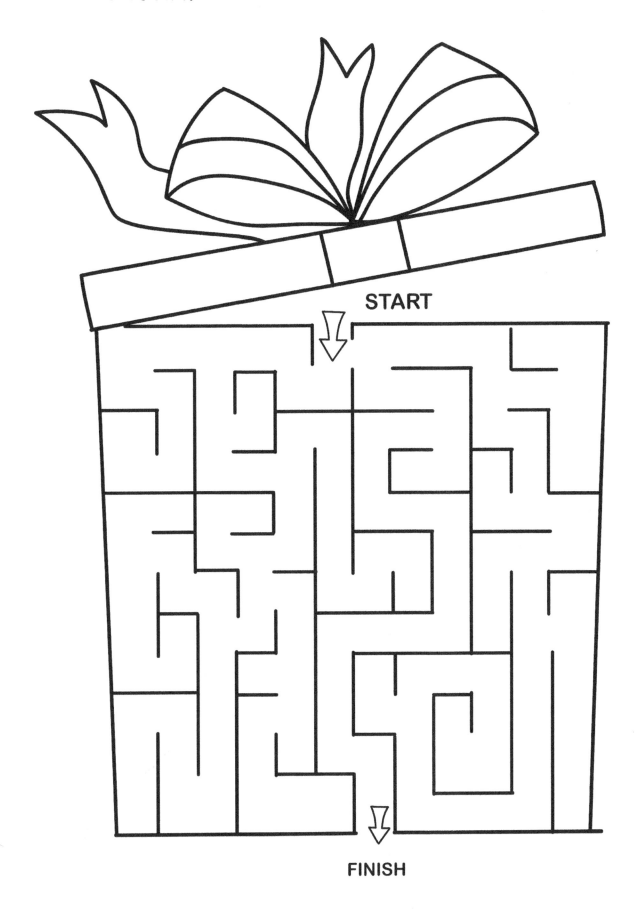

START

FINISH

TRACE THE DOTTED LINES AND COLOR THE PICTURE!

CHECK OUT OUR OTHER

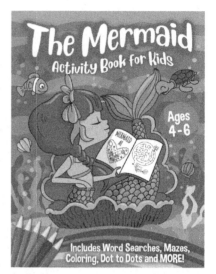

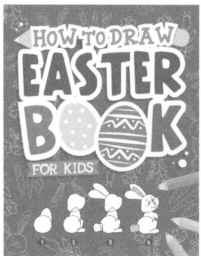

PEANUT PRODIGY

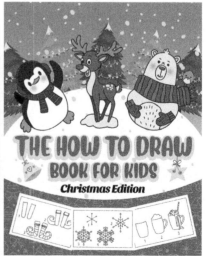

VISIT OUR AMAZON BOOK STORE AT:

PEANUT PRODIGY BOOKS!

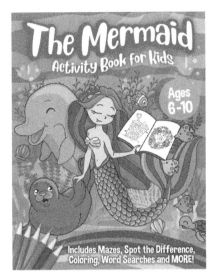

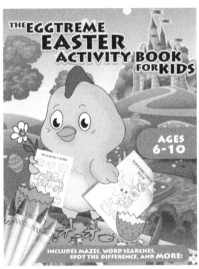

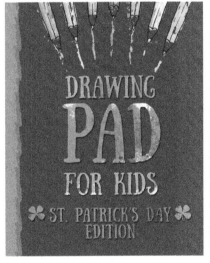

WWW.AMAZON.COM/AUTHOR/PEANUTPRODIGY

Made in the USA
Las Vegas, NV
09 December 2021

36905717R00033